Bond

English

Assessment Papers

8–9 years

OXFORD
UNIVERSITY PRESS

Great Clarendon Street, Oxford, OX2 6DP, United Kingdom

Oxford University Press is a department of the University of Oxford. It furthers the University's objective of excellence in research, scholarship,and education by publishing worldwide. Oxford is a registered trade mark of Oxford University Press in the UK and in certain other countries

Text © J M Bond and Sarah Lindsay 2015
Illustrations © Oxford University Press 2015

The moral rights of the authors have been asserted

First published in 2015

British Library Cataloguing in Publication Data
Data available

978-0-19-274002-1

10 9 8 7 6 5 4 3 2

Printed in China

Acknowledgements
The publishers would like to thank the following for permissions to use copyright material:

Illustrations: Nigel Kitching, K Kett and Beverly Curl
Page make-up: OKS Prepress, India
Cover illustrations: Lo Cole

Pp5–6 extract from *A House Called Awful End* by Philip Ardagh, copyright © 2002, published by Scholastic Ltd. Reprinted with permission by Faber and Faber Ltd and Henry Holt; p18 extract from *The Seven Voyages of Sinbad the Sailor* by John Yeoman, copyright © 2003, Chrysalis Children's Books; pp21–22 extract from *Blitz* © The Estate of Robert Westall 1994 reproduced by permission of Laura Cecil Literary Agency; p25 'Zanzibar' from *Walking on Air* by Berlie Doherty © 1993 Hodder Children's Books, reproduced by permission of David Higham Associates; p30 'Stopping by Woods on a Snowy Evening' from *The Poetry of Robert Frost* edited by Edward Connery Latham, published by Jonathan Cape. Reproduced by permission of the Random House Group Ltd; p36 extract from *Traitor* by Pete Johnson, published by Corgi Yearling. Reprinted by permission of the Random House Group Ltd; p39 extract from *The Copper Treasure* by Melvin Burgess published by A&C Black; pp45–46 extract from *Beaver Towers* by Nigel Hinton © 1995 Nigel Hinton. Reprinted by permission of Penguin Books Ltd; p52 'Billy Doesn't Like School Really' by Paul Cookson. Reproduced with permission of the author; pp55–56 'Ghost soup' from Kingfisher Treasury of Spooky Stories. Copyright © Kingfisher Publications Plc. Reproduced by permission of the publisher, all rights reserved.

Although we have made every effort to trace and contact all copyright holders before publication this has not been possible in all cases. If notified, the publisher will rectify any errors or omissions at the earliest opportunity.

Links to third party websites are provided by Oxford in good faith and for information only. Oxford disclaims any responsibility for the materials contained in any third party website referenced in this work.

Before you get started

What is Bond?

This book is part of the Bond Assessment Papers series for English, which provides **thorough and continuous practice of key English skills** from ages five to thirteen. Bond's English resources are ideal preparation for many different kinds of test and exam – from SATs to 11+ and other secondary school selection exams.

What does this book cover?

It practises comprehension, spelling, grammar, punctuation and vocabulary work appropriate for children of this age. It is fully in line with the National Curriculum for English and the National Literacy Strategy. One of the key features of Bond Assessment Papers is that each one practises **a wide variety of skills and question types** so that children are always challenged to think – and don't get bored repeating the same question type again and again. We think that variety is the key to effective learning. It helps children 'think on their feet' and cope with the unexpected.

The age given on the cover is for guidance only. As the papers are designed to be reasonably challenging for the age group, any one child may naturally find him or herself working above or below the stated age. The important thing is that children are always encouraged by their performance. Working at the right level is the key to this.

What does the book contain?

- **20 papers** – each one contains 40 questions.

- **Scoring devices** – there are score boxes in the margins and a Progress Chart on page 68. The chart is a visual and motivating way for children to see how they are doing. Encouraging them to colour in the chart as they go along and to try to beat their last score can be highly effective!

- **Next Steps** – advice on what to do after finishing the papers can be found on the inside back cover.

- **Answers** – located in an easily-removed central pull-out section.

- **Key English words** – on page 1 you will find a glossary of special key words that are used in the papers. These are highlighted in bold each time that they appear. These words are now used in the English curriculum and children are expected to know them at this age.

How can you use this book?

One of the great strengths of Bond Assessment Papers is their flexibility. They can be used at home, school and by tutors to:

- provide regular English practice in **bite-sized chunks**

- **highlight strengths and weaknesses** in the core skills

- identify **individual needs**

- set **homework**

- set **timed formal practice** tests – allow about 30 minutes.

It is best to start at the beginning and work though the papers in order.

What does a score mean and how can it be improved?

If children colour in the Progress Chart at the back, this will give an idea of how they are doing. The Next Steps inside the back cover will help you to decide what to do next to help a child progress. We suggest that it is always valuable to go over any wrong answers with children.

Don't forget the website...!

Visit www.bond11plus.co.uk for lots of advice, information and suggestions on everything to do with Bond and helping children to do their best.

Key words

adjectival phrase	a group of words describing a noun
adjective	a word that describes someone or something
adverb	a word that gives extra meaning to a verb
adverbial phrase	a word or phrase that makes the meaning of a verb, adjective or another adverb more specific, for example *The Cheshire cat vanished quite slowly beginning with the end of its tail.*
alphabetical order	the order found in the alphabet
antonym	a word with a meaning opposite to another word *hot – cold*
collective noun	a word referring to a group *swarm*
compound word	a word made up of two other words *football*
conjunction	a word used to link sentences, phrases and words *and*, *but*
consonant letters	all letters of the alphabet apart from a, e, i, o, u (vowel letters)
contraction	two words shortened into one with an apostrophe placed where the letter/s have been dropped *do not = don't*
definition	the meaning of a word
diminutive	a word implying smallness *booklet*
fronted adverbial	an adverbial that has been moved before the verb, for example *The day after tomorrow I'm going on holiday.*
homonym	a word that has the same spelling as another word, but a different meaning turn *left*, we *left* the room
homophone	a word that has the same sound as another, but a different meaning or spelling *right / write*
noun	a word for someone or something
past tense	form of a verb showing something that has already happened
personal pronoun	a pronoun used when writing about ourselves or others *I*, *you*, *he*
phrase	a group of words that act as a unit
plural	more than one *cats*
prefix	a group of letters added to the beginning of a word *un*, *dis*
present tense	form of a verb showing something happening now
pronoun	a word often replacing a noun
proper noun	the name of a person, place etc. *Ben*
root word	a word to which prefixes or suffixes can be added to make other words *quickly*
singular	one *cat*
suffix	a group of letters added to the end of a word *ly, ful*
syllables	the beats in a word
synonym	a word with a very similar meaning to another word *quick – fast*
verb	a 'doing' or 'being' word
vowel letters	the letters a, e, i, o, u

Rainforests

Tropical rainforests provide the richest habitat on Earth for living things.
They only cover 11 per cent of the planet's land surface but contain
over half its plant and animal species. Rainforests are found around the
Equator, in regions with a hot temperature all the year round and heavy
daily rainfall. The rainforests are found in South America, Central Africa,   5
South Asia and the Pacific islands.

The rainforest grows in a series of layers, reaching up to the light. Trees
can grow to heights of 25–45 metres. Their tops form the canopy, which
acts as a ceiling for the whole forest. It shields the forest against soil
erosion from heavy rain. Some individual trees grow above the canopy to   10
form an emergent layer. The further down the forest you go, the darker it
gets. Only 2 per cent of sunlight actually reaches the ground because of
the thick vegetation higher up.

Each layer supports its own special range of species. The canopy provides
a home for brightly coloured birds, such as toucans and macaws, and a   15
few mammals, such as sloths and monkeys. The layer below is called the
understory. Birds, butterflies, snakes and frogs inhabit this layer. Between
the understory and the forest floor, lies the shrub layer. This is made up
of ferns and small shrubs. The forest floor itself is the place where all the
dead plants and leaves rot down to make the soil that keeps the forest   20
alive. The larger animals live here: leopards and gorillas in Africa, tigers
and elephants in Asia, tapirs and jaguars in South America.

The rainforest is very fragile. It depends on the thin layer of soil for its
food. If the trees are cut down, the soil quickly becomes barren and
unable to support plant life again. It reverts to desert. At present the   25
rainforests are being destroyed at an alarming rate for timber. Perhaps
50 rainforest species are becoming extinct every day. The tribal people
who live in the forests are being displaced. Forest destruction is one
cause of the warming of the whole planet.

Underline the right answers.

1 Which of these continents does not contain rainforests?

(Asia, Africa, Europe, South America)

2 Which of these species live in the understory?

(macaws, sloths, butterflies, monkeys)

3 The rainforest is being cut down for (space, timber, light)

Answer these questions.

4 How does the canopy protect the rainforest?

_____

5 Write these layers of the rainforest in order, topmost one first:

shrub layer, emergent layer, understory, forest floor, canopy.

(1) _____ (2) _____ (3) _____

(4) _____ (5) _____

6 What does 'fragile' in line 23 mean?

_____

7 What does 'displaced' in line 28 mean?

_____

8–9 Give two reasons why cutting down trees in the rainforest is damaging.

_____

_____

Underline a **noun** in each line.

10 pretty   book   went   she   busy

11 it   large   ready   new   desk

12 brown   Wednesday   ran   some   our

13 legs   dirty   them   broken   their

14 interesting   house   long   dull   her

15 from   Hannah   get   old   tipped

16 paper   badly   sad   come   too

Spell these words correctly. Each word has missing vowels.

17 y_____ _____ng

18 c_____ _____ntry

19 tr_____ _____bl_____

20 t_____ _____ch

21 d_____ _____bl_____

5

Add a sequence word at the beginning of each sentence so that it makes sense.

While   After   Then   First

22–25 _____ Tina sat in her chair while her teacher took the

register. _____ she copied some sentences from the board.

_____ her teacher collected in the homework, Tina was writing.

_____ she had finished copying the sentences she was allowed

out to play.

4

Circle the words that have two **syllables**.

26–31

fall   bellow   arrow   eel

puppet   sparrow   wobble

pill   tree   pillow

6

Rewrite the short passage, putting in the missing capital letters and full-stops.

32–40 mr scott visited edinburgh and glasgow each friday then he travelled on the overnight train to london

_____

_____

_____

9

Now go to the Progress Chart to record your score!   Total   40

4

When Eddie Dickens was eleven years old, both his parents caught some awful disease that made them turn yellow, go a bit crinkly around the edges, and smell of old hot-water bottles.

There were lots of diseases like that in those days. Perhaps it had something to do with all that thick fog, those knobbly cobbled streets and the fact that everyone went everywhere by horse … even to the bathroom. Who knows?

'It's very contagious,' said his father.

'And catching,' said his mother, sucking on an ice cube shaped like a famous general.

They were in Eddie's parents' bedroom, which was very dark and dingy and had no furniture in it except for a large double bed, an even larger wardrobe, and thirty-two different types of chair designed to make you sit up straight even if your wrists were handcuffed to your ankles.

'Why are you sucking an ice cube shaped like a famous general?' Eddie asked his parents, who were propped up against piles of pillows in their impressively ugly double bed.

'Doctor Muffin says that it helps with the swelling,' said his mother. In fact, because she had a famous-general-shaped ice cube in her mouth, what she actually said was, 'Dotter Muffin schez va it hewlpz wiva schwelln,' but Eddie managed to translate.

'What swelling?' he asked politely.

His mother shrugged, then suddenly looked even more yellow and even more crinkly round the edges.

'And why do they have to be famous-general-shaped?' asked Eddie. He always asked lots of questions and whenever he asked lots of questions his father would say: 'Questions! Questions!'

'Questions! Questions!' said his father.

Told you.

(Line numbers in right margin: 5, 10, 15, 20, 25)

'But why a famous general?' Eddie repeated. 'Surely the shape of the   *30*
ice cube can't make any difference?'

'Schows sow muck chew no,' muttered his mother, which meant (and
still means), 'Shows how much you know.'

His father rustled the bedclothes. 'One does not question the good
doctor,' he said. 'Especially when one is a child.' He was a small man   *35*
except for when he was sitting up in bed. In this position, he looked
extremely tall.

Then Eddie's mother rustled the bedclothes. It was easy to make them
rustle because they were made entirely from brown paper bags glued
together with those extra strips of gummed paper you sometimes get if   *40*
you buy more than one stamp at the post office.

Postage stamps were a pretty new idea back then, and everyone
– except for a great-great-great-aunt on my mother's side of the family
– was excited about them.

From *A House Called Awful End* by Philip Ardagh

Underline the right answers.

1 Why did Eddie think there were lots of diseases 'in those days'?

(because it was cold, because people did not eat enough, because it
was foggy)

2 Eddie's parents' bedroom had (no, a little, lots of) furniture in it.

3 Why had Doctor Muffin recommended chewing ice cubes?

(because they were cool, because they were easy to make, because
they helped with a swelling)

⬤ 3

Answer these questions.

4 What happened to Eddie's parents when he was eleven?

_____

5 What does 'contagious' mean in line 8?

_____

6 Why was it easy to rustle the bedclothes?

_____

7–8 List two details from the story that show that it was set a long time
ago.

_____

_____

9 Say in your own words why you think this is going to be a rather strange story.

_____

6

Underline the two **antonyms** in each line.

10 right   back   left   correct

11 dark   light   day   winter

12 young   happy   dirty   clean

13 funny   rich   poor   ill

14 danger   safety   crash   freedom

15 here   now   then   where

6

Add the missing commas to these sentences.

16 Diane is making a blouse a skirt and a dress.

17–18 Steven bought some potatoes carrots cabbages and onions.

19–21 At school we study English mathematics history geography and art.

6

Add the **suffix** _ness_ or _ment_ to each of these words.

22 weak_____   **23** agree_____

24 pay_____   **25** enjoy_____

26 blind_____   **27** state_____

28 quiet_____   **29** ill_____

8

Underline an **adjective** that best describes the word in bold.

30 station   three   pink   heavy   busy

31 pencil   wet   sharp   sleepy   hot

32 hands   ten   happy   clean   first

33 June   sunny   foggy   dark   frosty

34 hair   sticky   sweet   quiet   straight

8

Match each word with its meaning. Write the number next to the word.

35 carrot   _____   (1) a funny picture

36 carpet   _____   (2) he makes things out of wood

37 carton   _____   (3) a vegetable

38 cartoon   _____   (4) a cardboard box

39 carol   _____   (5) floor covering

40 carpenter   _____   (6) a song   **6**

Now go to the Progress Chart to record your score!   Total   **40**

Paper 3

Scene 1

Mr Williams' classroom
Writing on blackboard – 'Mr Williams
is a silly old fool'

Mark and Andy are playing in Mr Williams' classroom during playtime.
They should have been outside. Suddenly they hear footsteps coming
down the corridor.

Mark   Quick! Hide! He is coming, I can hear his footsteps.
Andy   Where? He has eyes in the back of his head. Even if we
                  hide he will know we are here.
Mark   We must try – what about the store cupboard?

They both rush over to the store cupboard.

Footsteps getting closer.

Mark   It's locked.
Andy   Hurry up! Under Mr Williams' table.

Mark and Andy sitting under table.

Mark   I wish I hadn't written anything on the blackboard!

Sound of two sets of footsteps coming into the room.

Andy	*(whispering and peering under the desk)* It's not Mr Williams, it's a woman. I can see the legs. I think it's Mrs Wilkinson. She wears those shoes with the flat buckles. And there's someone else there. It looks like Miss Jones – black trousers, blue shoes with laces.
Mrs Wilkinson	*(to Miss Jones)* Now we're alone, Caroline, we can discuss the matter. *(suddenly catches sight of the board and laughs.)* He is too. Should have retired years ago, silly old fool. We'd better wipe it off though ... Anyway, as I was saying, what happened?
Miss Jones	Well, I left my handbag in the staff room and when I went back to look for it, the Head was coming out, very quickly, holding a large supermarket bag.
Mrs Wilkinson	Well, Caroline? So what?
Miss Jones	When I looked in the staff room, my handbag was gone.

Underline the right answers.

1 Which scene of the play is this?

(Scene 1, Scene 2, don't know)

2 Where did the boys first want to hide?

(behind a desk, under the teacher's table, in the store cupboard)

3 Miss Jones wore (flat shoes with a buckle, blue shoes with laces, trainers)

3

Answer these questions.

4 Why couldn't the boys hide in the cupboard?

_____

5 What was Miss Jones's first name?

_____

6 What made Mrs Wilkinson laugh?

_____

7 What was Miss Jones suggesting the Head might have done?

_____

8–9 What do you think happens next?

_____

_____

6

Circle the words that are spelt correctly.

10–13   enough   quater

              exersise   naughty

              oposite   importent

         interest   striaght   promise   ◯ 4

Name the **collective noun** for each of the following.

14 twelve cows   _____

15 a large number of wasps   _____

16 a large area of trees   _____

17 a handful of flowers   _____

18 a group of sheep   _____

19 a side of football players   _____   ◯ 6

Arrange these words in the order you would find them in the dictionary.

          colour   dark   eel   dragon   egg   change

20 (1) _____   **21** (2) _____   **22** (3) _____

23 (4) _____   **24** (5) _____   **25** (6) _____   ◯ 6

Underline the fronted adverbial in each of these sentences.

26 Before we leave, make sure you have been to the toilet.

27 The day after tomorrow, I'm going to Australia

28 Later that morning. I heard the school had flooded.

Write three sentences that begin with a fronted adverbial.

29 _____

30 _____

31 _____   ◯ 6

Rewrite the **proper nouns** with capital letters.

swamp   birmingham   prince william   dexter

august   chester   block   monday   tap

abigail   mrs jones   magician   thursday

32 _____   33 _____   34 _____

35 _____   36 _____   37 _____

38 _____   39 _____   40 _____   ◯ 9

Paper 4

Strange, strange, is the little old man
Who lives in the Grange.
Old, old, and they say that he keeps
A box full of gold.
Bowed, bowed, is his thin little back   5
Which once was so proud.
Soft, soft, are his steps as he climbs
The stairs to the loft.
Black, black, is the old shuttered house.
Does he sleep on a sack?   10
They say he does magic, that he can cast spells,
That he prowls round the garden listening for bells;
That he watches for strangers, hates every soul,
And peers with his dark eye through the keyhole.
I wonder, I wonder, as I lie in my bed,   15
Whether he sleeps with his hat on his head?
Is he really a magician with altar of stone
Or a lonely old gentleman left on his own?

Underline the right answers.

    1 The man is (small, tall, medium height).

    2 People say he keeps (jewels, gold, silver, pennies) in a box.

    3 He walks upstairs (quietly, quickly, noisily).

Answer these questions.

    4 What do people say he can do?

_____

    5 What do people say he listens for?

_____

3

6 What is a 'loft'?

_____

7–8 Write two words that describe the man.

_____   _____

9 If the man is not a magician, what could he be?

_____

Add the correct **homophone** in each sentence.

10 hear or **here**   I can _____ the train coming.

11 write or **right**   Sam got all the answers _____.

12 stares or **stairs**   Grandpa climbed the _____ one at a time.

13 saw or **sore**   Kate _____ the horse galloping.

14 road or **rowed**   Tuhil and Frank _____ as fast as they could.

15 Witch or **Which**   _____ cake shall I have?

Underline the words that are spoken in these sentences.

16 "Quick, come here!" yelled the teacher.

17 "I'm waiting for my tea," answered Greg.

18 The children muttered, "Wish we didn't have to go to bed!"

19 "Shh, the baby is asleep," whispered Dad.

20 "You do look silly!" laughed Rupa.

Rewrite these sentences, making the **plurals singular**.

21 The trees swayed in the wind.

_____

22–23 The boys ate the sweets.

_____

24 The barking dogs scared the girl.

_____

25–27 Sophie collected the ponies and led them to the buckets of food.

_____ 7

Make eight **compound words** out of the eleven short words.

card   worm   butter   man   cup   ball

snow   earth   post   egg   board

28 _____ **29** _____

30 _____ **31** _____

32 _____ **33** _____

34 _____ **35** _____ 8

Write _am_, _is_ or _are_ in the sentence so that it makes sense.

36 They _____ going to the beach.

37 I _____ really going to miss you.

38 We _____ going to have a ride tomorrow.

39 David _____ very upset.

40 The twins _____ sharing a bedroom. 5

BIGVILLE WEEKLY ECHO

Homes facing the bulldozer

by Mike Smeaton

Heartbroken council tenants in the Nanton area of Bigville have little to celebrate over Christmas. They have just been told that their houses could be demolished because the council does not have the money to repair them.

The council recently surveyed 80 Westway type houses and found they were in very poor condition. They have severe structural problems and the repair bill has been put at 4.8 million.

Westway houses have steel frames and were built in large numbers to meet Britain's population growth in the 1950s. The houses were prefabricated in sections in the factory and bolted together on site. It was a quick and cheap solution to Britain's housing problem after the war. For speed, chemicals were used to harden the concrete. It was found in the 1980s that when exposed to water, the chemicals rotted the steel. Repairs were done in the 1990s to slow down the decay, but now the council thinks the damage is beyond repair. 'We simply don't have the funds to repair the houses any more,' said John Kennaway, the council engineer. 'Anyway it would be a very difficult task.'

Local residents are confused and angry. 'Quite honestly, it's made for a terrible Christmas,' said Jane Adams, who has lived in Ringway Close for 51 years. 'Many of us have lived here all our lives. I love my home and it's not just buildings that we're talking about. A whole community could be destroyed.'

Mrs Adams, who chairs the Residents' Association, said that the money should be found to preserve the houses. The council says it simply does not have the cash. Jeff Johnston, the councillor for housing, said there was no easy solution. Part of the problem is that the houses are semi-detached and some of them have been sold to private owners. If it wanted to bulldoze them, the council would have to buy back the privately owned houses first.

Underline the right answers.

1 Westway houses were built (before the war, during the war, after the war).

2 What is Jeff Johnston's job?

(councillor for housing, chair of the Residents' Association, council engineer)

3 Westway homes are (detached, bungalows, semi-detached).

3

Answer these questions.

4 What reason is given for Britain's housing problem after the war?

_____

5 Why were chemicals useful in building Westway houses?

_____

6 What does 'prefabricated' in line 19 mean?

_____

7 Write two words to describe how local residents feel about the problem.

(1) _____   (2) _____

8 Why doesn't Jane Adams want the houses destroyed?

_____

9–10 Give two reasons why the council cannot repair the houses.

(1) _____

(2) _____

11 Explain in your own words what Mrs Adams meant when she said 'A whole community could be destroyed' (lines 42–43).

_____

8

Spell each of these words correctly.

12 vien   **13** thay

14 nieghbour   **15** wiegh

16 obay   **17** eghty-eight

6

Circle the **pronouns** in each sentence.

18–19 They thought he sang beautifully.

20–21 It was the best day he could remember.

22–23 He said she was very clever.

24–25 They screamed to make him hear.

⬭ 8

Underline the **root word** in each of these words.

26 dislike   **27** jumping   **28** unkind

29 frighten   **30** passed   **31** altogether

⬭ 6

Rewrite these two sentences, adding the missing punctuation and capital letters.

32–36 david was unsure what day it was was it thursday

_____

_____

⬭ 5

Underline a **synonym** for the word in bold.

37 pointed	shiny	sharp	dull	sloping
38 circle	square	peg	round	oblong
39 nation	country	ribbon	food	strip
40 busy	lazy	hard	soft	active

⬭ 4

My father, who was a very rich merchant, died when I was
still a child, leaving me enormous wealth and property and
land. When I became a young man and could get my hands on
the money, I spent and spent on expensive clothes and fine living,
treating all my friends to the very best of everything – as if the money   5
would last forever. But finally I came to my senses and realised that if I
carried on in this way I should soon be facing poverty.

So I resolved to do something about it. I sold my remaining
possessions and fine clothes for three thousand dirhams, enough to fund
me for a journey to foreign parts. And with the money I bought some   10
goods to trade with and all I needed for a long voyage, and joined a
company of merchants on board a vessel bound for Basra, where we
changed ship. We sailed for weeks on end, travelling through the Persian
Gulf and into the Arabian Sea, going from island to island, until finally we
reached an island that looked just like the gardens of Paradise.   15

We cast anchor and landed, and in no time we were busying ourselves
in our different ways: making ovens in the sand, cooking, washing,
exploring, and playing games to amuse ourselves. At one point I thought
I felt a small earth tremor, but nobody else seemed to notice it. They just
carried on with what they were doing. I went off with a small group to   20
explore, but we hadn't ventured very far before we heard the ship's
captain hailing us from the gunwale at the top of his voice.

'Run for your lives!' he was calling. 'Drop everything and get back on
board. This isn't an island, after all. We've landed on a monstrous fish
that's been asleep so long that the sands have settled over it and the   25
trees have sprung up on it. But when you lit your fires it felt the heat and
began to stir. At any moment it will plunge down into the depths, taking
you all with it. Get back to the ship before you drown!'

We didn't need any persuading, I can tell you. We abandoned our
bundles of merchandise, our spare clothes, our cooking pots, and   30
everything else in our mad scramble back to the ship.

From *The Seven Voyages of Sinbad the Sailor* by John Yeoman

Underline the right answers.

1 The father of the person in the story had been a (sailor, merchant, soldier, fisherman).

2 Which of these seas did the ship sail to?

(the Indian Ocean, the Black Sea, the Arabian Sea, the Pacific Ocean, the Persian Gulf)

3 The fish woke up because of (an earth tremor, the shouting of the men, the fires).

3

Answer these questions.

4 Say in your own words why the person in the story needed to change his life.

_____

5 What does 'resolved' mean in line 8?

_____

6 Why did the passengers and crew not notice they had landed on a fish?

_____

7 What warning did the person telling the story have that there was something strange about the island?

_____

8 How do you think the people felt when they discovered that they weren't on an island?

_____

5

Add the **prefix** or **suffix** al to each of these words.

9 _____ways_____   10 _____historic_____   11 _____so_____

12 _____ready_____   13 _____mechanic_____   14 _____medic_____

15 _____accident_____   16 _____though_____   17 _____most_____

9

Write each of these verbs in the **past tense**.

18 walk _____   **19** jump _____

20 pull _____   **21** sprint _____

22 push _____   **23** listen _____

◯ 6

Put one of the **conjunctions** in each of the spaces below.

until   but   because   so

24 Marianne stayed at home _____ she had a cold.

25 The sea is quite warm _____ we can go swimming.

26 Mum is going out now _____ she will be back soon.

27 'Don't eat the biscuit _____ you've finished your lunch.'

28 We will stay here _____ dad asked us to.

◯ 5

Write the *nch* or *tch* word to match each picture.

29

l_____

30

i_____

31

s_____

32

b_____

33

p_____

34

s_____

◯ 6

Using a line, match each word with its correct **definition**.

35 voyage   every year

36 remedy   a long journey

37 summit   a piece broken off something

38 annual   a large, deep spoon

39 ladle   a cure

40 fragment   the top

◯ 6

Now go to the Progress Chart to record your score!   Total ◯ 40

Rosie hurried on. The pubs were further apart now and even the alleys were silent. Just the odd moggie, poor things, scavenging at the pigswill bins.

She was just bending down to stroke one when the siren went. For the third time that day. Rosie got the usual sinking feeling in her gut, but she wasn't all that worried. Air-raid sirens couldn't kill you. She listened intently, through the dying drone of the siren, for the sound of bombers' engines…

And heard nothing.

She'd carry on for a bit, try and get home before anything happened. Her ma would worry if she was caught out in a raid. Ma might even leave the shelter and come looking for her, as far as the chippie in Scobie Street. Then batter Rosie over the ear when she found her, for causing so much worry.

'G'night, moggie. Best of British Luck!'

Her footsteps quickened; the gas mask banged harder against her bottom, as if urging her on.

She'd gone nearly half a mile before she heard the bombers coming. She was in a district she hardly knew. Really poor people, to judge from the state of their doors and windows. But you couldn't be choosy when the bombers came. You just ran for the nearest brick street-shelter with its concrete-slab roof.

Not many shelters round here. Poor people were always the worst looked after. Bet the toffs had shelters, and to spare, up Croxteth way …

She ran and ran. Turned a corner by a chapel with bombed-out windows. Saw the three brass balls of a pawnbroker's… Then a great square shelter loomed up.

She made the doorway, just as the first guns opened up overhead, turning the night white-black, white-black. Making a noise like some daft kid banging a tin tray right in your ear that echoed across the whole sky after.

Then she heard the shrapnel shrieking down like dead rockets on Bonfire Night. And ducked through the blackout curtain into the shelter.

There was room by the door, on the slatted benches… She flung herself into it, to get her breath back…

Still panting, she looked around.

35

And sighed. It seemed a totally miserable sort of shelter.

People huddled together in a dim blue light. Silent except for the racking cough and the dismal wail of a baby at the far end.

From *Blitz* by Robert Westall

Underline the right answers.

1 What was Rosie doing when the siren went?

(looking for shelter, looking in pigswill bins, stroking a moggie)

2 She was carrying (a suitcase, a gas mask, an umbrella).

3 The guns sounded like (dead rockets, a tray being banged, the sea hitting cliffs).

◯ 3

Answer these questions.

4 How did Rosie feel when she heard the sirens?

_____

5 Why did Rosie think that her mother might hit her round the head?

_____

6 How could Rosie tell that she had come to a poor area?

_____

7 Who do you think the 'toffs' are in line 24?

_____

8 Describe in your own words what made the shelter seem so miserable.

_____

◯ 5

Put these words in the **past tense**.

9 go _____

10 sing _____

11 jump _____

12 fight _____

13 buy _____

14 come _____

◯ 6

Rewrite these sentences using a more interesting phrase than the words in bold.

15 We had a good time at the **party**.

_____

16 My **teacher** is very grumpy.

_____

17 Daniel climbed out of the **pool** and got dressed.

_____

18 The **baby** screamed until it was picked up.

_____

19 The **children** had a fun day.

_____

20 Joseph was reading a **book**.

_____   ◯ 6

Add the ly suffix to each of these words.

21 grumpy   _____   **22** poor   _____

23 sad   _____   **24** quick   _____

25 kind   _____   **26** happy   _____

27 stupid   _____   **28** rough   _____   ◯ 6

Many railway lines link London with other parts of the country. There are two main lines to Scotland: one goes up the east side of the country through York and Newcastle, and the other goes up the west side, passing through Crewe and Carlisle. If you are travelling to North Wales you leave the main line at Crewe. There are fast trains from Liverpool, Manchester and Sheffield to London and it is much easier to travel from north to south than it is to travel from east to west. There is a fast service from London to the West Country which passes through Salisbury and Exeter. There is an excellent electric service between London and south-east England.

Underline the right answers.

29–30 Which two of these towns would you pass through if you were travelling from London to Scotland on the east side of the country? (Crewe, York, Salisbury, Manchester, Carlisle, Newcastle)

31 Which direction is it easier to travel in? (east to west, north to south)

Answer these questions.

32 If you were travelling to North Wales, where do you leave the main line?

_____

33–34 Name two cities that have fast trains to London.

_____   _____

35 What is the service like between London and south-east England?

_____

Add the missing commas to these sentences where a short pause or pauses are needed.

36–37 Harry a very nervous boy hated the thunderstorm.

38 The boys set off along the track anxious to get to the next village before dark.

39 Najib ran as fast as he could barely taking a breath.

40 Leena was starving having not had anything to eat all day.

Paper 8

Zanzibar

Zanzibar used to make me think
Of marzipan and stripes.
It has the sounds of bees in it, and zizz.

I didn't know it would smell of spice
of lemon grass and strips of cinnamon   5
green balls of pepper,

buds of cloves,
nutmeg and vanilla pods
and rain, and steamy rain.

Children cling beneath banana leaves   10
and splash home, laughing, through the mud.
Soon the rain will wash their homes away.

Their mothers watch the sky.
When the sun dries the earth
They will squat and scoop and daub   15
and build their huts again.

Zanzibar. Palm trees and red skies
Blue fireflies in the night
Cinnamon, cloves, and lemon grass, and rain.

by Berlie Doherty

Underline the right answers.

1 Zanzibar is (a colour, a smell, a sound, a place).

2 Which of these smells does the poet not mention?

(vanilla, cinnamon, nutmeg, ginger, cloves)

3 At night in the poem you can see (stars, fireflies, the moon, the sea).

3

Answer these questions.

4 Find something that is green in the poem and something that is red.

_____

5 What is the weather like in Zanzibar?

_____

6 Why do the mothers need to watch the skies in Zanzibar?

_____

7 Why might the sound of the word 'Zanzibar' remind the author of the sound of bees?

_____

8 Do you think that the poet has been to Zanzibar? Use evidence from the poem to support your answer.

_____

5

Write the missing **noun** with an apostrophe to show something belongs to someone.

9 The rabbit belonged to Dimitri. It was _____ rabbit.

10 The crayons belonged to Jane. They were _____ crayons.

11 The jacket belonged to Helen. It was _____ jacket.

12 The bone belonged to Mop the dog. It was _____ bone.

13 The rat belonged to Rajeeh. It was _____ rat.

14 The books belonged to Soraya. They were _____ books.

6

Write each of these words correctly. A letter in each word needs to be changed to a y.

15 mith _____   **16** gim _____

17 Egipt _____   18 mistery _____

19 piramid _____

5

Circle the **nouns** that don't have a different **plural** form.

20–23

reindeer   gate   grapefruit   jacket

goldfish   fork   sheep   button

5

Underline a **synonym** for the word in bold.

24 **aid**	act	hinder	help	stop
25 **drop**	rain	prod	bounce	fall
26 **sad**	strict	unhappy	glad	ugly
27 **quick**	loud	fast	slow	quiet
28 **several**	few	both	some	none
29 **enjoy**	hate	like	suffer	drive
30 **modern**	new	old	ancient	great
31 **depart**	post	leave	come	send

8

Write the **plural** of each of these **nouns** ending in *f*.

32 hoof _____   33 shelf _____

34 loaf _____   35 calf _____

36 leaf _____   37 wolf _____

6

Write an interesting sentence about each of the following.

38 your home

_____

39 your hair

_____

40 your teacher

_____

3

Now go to the Progress Chart to record your score!   Total   40

Paper 9

How to make a Christmas pudding

You need:

1 cup plain flour

1 tablespoon mixed spice

$\frac{2}{3}$ cup brown sugar

3 cups mixed dried fruit

A pinch of salt

1 cup shredded suet

1 large egg, beaten

$\frac{1}{2}$ cup brown ale

Butter or margarine to grease the basin

1 Get a large mixing bowl. Mix everything in the bowl except the egg and the ale.
2 Add the egg and the ale. Stir them in. Put the mixture in a cool place and cover with a cloth. Leave for a day.
3 Grease a 900 ml/1.5 pint pudding basin. Cut out a circle of non-stick baking paper and line the bottom of the basin.
4 Stir the pudding again and tip it into the basin. Cover with a circle of greaseproof paper. Put an old saucer over the top. Then cover it with a double thickness of foil. Fold it over the edge of the basin all the way round. Tie string round to hold it on tight over the basin.
5 Put the basin into a steamer over a pan of boiling water. Cover with a lid. Steam the pudding for 6 hours. **Caution: you must check the steamer every half an hour to make sure there is enough boiling water in the pan. Top it up as needed.**
6 Re-cover the pudding. Store it in a cool place. Steam it for another 2.5 hours before serving it. Happy Christmas!

Write true or false by each of these statements.

1 You must have brandy to go in the pudding. _____

2 You put the butter or margarine into the mixture. _____

3 You need a rolling pin to make the pudding. _____

4 You need to beat the egg before you put it in. _____

5 You need to line the basin before you pour the mixture in. _____

6 Putting a string round the pudding basin helps to carry it. _____

7 You can make a Christmas pudding in a day. _____

7

Answer this question.

8 What do you think will happen if you do not check the steamer every half an hour while the pudding is cooking?

_____

Write a more powerful **verb** for each of the verbs in bold.

9 Harry **walked** to Gary's house. _____

10 "May I have a cake?" **said** Meena. _____

11 Dave **took** his pen back from Ann. _____

12 "Please can I watch television?" **said** Nigel. _____

13 The man **ran** round the park. _____

5

Put these words correctly into the table.

chef   echo
          character
          machine
scheme   brochure

14–19

words with...	
ch sounding 'sh' as in shout	ch sounding 'c' as in cat

6

The following sentences are not in the right order. Read them through carefully, and then write the numbers to show their correct order.

20 _____ (1) The cyclist lay on the road.

21 _____ (2) Then the policeman called for an ambulance.

22 _____ (3) A cyclist was knocked off his bicycle.

23 _____ (4) Finally the cyclist was taken to hospital.

24 _____ (5) Meanwhile a policeman arrived.

25 _____ (6) Next the ambulance arrived.

5

With a line, join each word with its **diminutive** (word implying smallness).

26	owl	duckling
27	cat	piglet
28	goose	owlet
29	pig	bullock
30	duck	kitten
31	bull	gosling

6

Rewrite the sentences, adding in the missing punctuation and capital letters.

32–35 the plane landed at heathrow airport a little late

_____

36–40 tessa and claire admitted they were lost what were they going to do

_____

9

Now go to the Progress Chart to record your score! **Total** 40

Paper 10

Stopping by Woods on a Snowy Evening

Whose woods these are I think I know.
His house is in the village, though;
He will not see me stopping here
To watch his woods fill up with snow.

My little horse must think it queer   5
To stop without a farmhouse near
Between the woods and frozen lake
The darkest evening of the year.

He gives his harness bells a shake
To ask if there is some mistake.   10
The only other sound's the sweep
Of easy wind and downy flake.

The woods are lovely, dark, and deep,
But I have promises to keep,
And miles to go before I sleep,   15
And miles to go before I sleep.

by Robert Frost

30

Underline the right answers.

1 At what time of day is this poem set?

(morning, afternoon, evening)

2 Where does the owner of the woods live?

(in a farmhouse, in the woods, in a village)

3 Where does the rider stop his horse?

(in the woods, beside the woods, a long way from the woods) ⬤ 3

Answer these questions.

4–5 Describe two sounds the rider can hear.

(1) _____

(2) _____

6 Why would the rider's horse think it 'queer' to stop where they have?

_____

7 Which line in the poem tells you that the rider loves the woods, rather than is frightened of them?

_____

8 How do you think you would feel about the woods if you were making the same journey? Why?

_____ ⬤ 5

Write the word or words each of these **contractions** is made from.

9 should've _____   10 won't _____

11 I'll _____   12 can't _____

13 they've _____   14 isn't _____

15 wouldn't _____   16 haven't _____ ⬤ 8

31

Add the missing speech marks to these sentences.

17 Have you found the dog? asked Jim.

18 Let's go and play in the park, suggested Aman.

19 I don't think you have washed your face! joked Dad.

20 Are you enjoying the pizza? asked the waitress.

21 I wish it would stop raining, sighed Amy.

22 Where do you think you are going? asked Mrs Thrower.   6

Rewrite the word adding the **suffix** *ible* or *able*. (Remember, if the last letter of the word is a vowel, the last letter is usually dropped before adding the suffix.)

23 suit _____

24 reason _____

25 sense _____

26 believe _____

27 wash _____

28 response _____   6

Underline the **adverbs** in these sentences.

29 The old man shouted angrily at the children.

30 The child ran noisily along the corridor.

31 The cat slowly stretched her leg.

32 Billy neatly wrote the date at the top of the page.

33 The robin sang sweetly as the snow fell.

34 My Dad snored loudly in front of the television.   6

With a line, match a word in each column to make a **compound word**. Write the compound words.

over	room	35 _____
moon	fall	36 _____
some	head	37 _____
water	light	38 _____
drain	where	39 _____
class	pipe	40 _____

6

Now go to the Progress Chart to record your score!   Total   40

32

Some questions will be answered in the children's own words. Answers to these questions are given in *italics*. Any answers that seem to be in line with these should be marked correct.

Paper 1

1 Europe
2 butterflies
3 timber
4 It shields the forest against soil erosion from heavy rain.
5 (1) emergent layer (2) canopy (3) understory (4) shrub layer (5) forest floor
6 *easily broken, delicate*
7 *moved on*
8–9 Two of the following: *the soil becomes barren/goes back to desert; species become extinct; tribal people are displaced; it helps to cause global warming.*
10 book   11 desk
12 Wednesday 13 legs
14 house   15 Hannah
16 paper   17 young
18 country   19 trouble
20 touch   21 double
22 First   23 Then
24 While   25 After
26–31 bellow, arrow, puppet, sparrow, wobble, pillow
32–40 **M**r **S**cott visited **E**dinburgh and **G**lasgow each **F**riday**.** **T**hen he travelled on the overnight train to **L**ondon**.**

Paper 2

1 because it was foggy
2 lots of
3 because they helped with a swelling
4 *They caught an awful disease, went crinkly round the edges, smelled of old hot-water bottles.*
5 *Catching*
6 *They were made out of brown paper bags.*
7–8 Two of the following: *the thick fog, the cobbled streets, everyone used horses, postage stamps were a new idea.*

9 Answers should mention the nonsense elements in the story: *everyone went to the bathroom on horses, the famous-general-shaped ice cubes, the large number of pieces of furniture in the bedroom, the bedclothes made out of brown paper bags.*
10 right, left   11 dark, light
12 dirty, clean   13 rich, poor
14 danger, safety 15 now, then
16 Diane is making a blouse**,** a skirt and a dress**.**
17–18 Steven bought some potatoes**,** carrots**,** cabbages and onions**.**
19–21 At school we study English**,** mathematics**,** history**,** geography and art**.**
22 weakness   23 agreement
24 payment   25 enjoyment
26 blindness   27 statement
28 quietness   29 illness
30 busy   31 sharp
32 clean   33 sunny
34 straight   35 (3)
36 (5)   37 (4)
38 (1)   39 (6)
40 (2)

Paper 3

1 Scene 1
2 in the store cupboard
3 blue shoes with laces
4 It was locked.
5 Caroline
6 *The writing on the board made her laugh because she agreed with it.*
7 *She was suggesting that the Head had stolen her bag.*
8–9 *Child's own interpretation of what might happen next.*
10–13 enough   naughty   promise   interest
14 herd   15 swarm
16 forest/wood 17 bunch
18 flock   19 team
20 change   21 colour
22 dark   23 dragon

24 eel

25 egg

26 <u>Before we leave</u>, make sure you have been to the toilet.

27 <u>The day after tomorrow</u>, I'm going to Australia.

28 <u>Later that morning</u>, I heard the school had flooded.

29–31 *Child's own examples of fronted adverbials written into sentences.*

32–40 Birmingham, Prince William, Dexter, August, Chester, Monday, Abigail, Mrs Jones, Thursday

Paper 4

1 small

2 gold

3 quietly

4 *He can do magic, cast spells*

5 *He listens for bells*

6 *It is the room at the top of the house*

7–8 *old, strange, little, thin, lonely, bowed*

9 *a lonely old gentleman*

10 hear   11 right

12 stairs   13 saw

14 rowed   15 Which

16 "<u>Quick, come here!</u>" yelled the teacher.

17 "<u>I'm waiting for my tea</u>," answered Greg.

18 The children muttered, "<u>Wish we didn't have to go to bed!</u>"

19 "<u>Shh, the baby is asleep</u>," whispered Dad.

20 "<u>You do look silly!</u>" laughed Rupa.

21 The tree swayed in the wind.

22–23 The boy ate the sweet.

24 The barking dog scared the girl.

25–27 Sophie collected the pony and led it to the bucket of food.

28–35 *cardboard, earthworm, buttercup, postman, snowball, postcard, eggcup, cupboard, snowboard, snowman*

36 are   37 am

38 are   39 is

40 are

Paper 5

1 after the war

2 councillor for housing

3 semi-detached

4 The population grew.

5 *They helped to harden concrete quickly; helped the houses to be made more quickly.*

6 *Made in advance.*

7 Two from: *heartbroken, confused, angry, upset.*

8 *She has lived there all her life. She loves her home. It would destroy the whole community.*

9–10 It does not have the money; Some of the homes have been sold to private owners.

11 *Mrs Adams meant that if the houses were torn down, then the people who lived in them would have to move and the friendships they'd built would be destroyed.*

12 vein

13 they

14 neighbour

15 weigh

16 obey

17 eighty-eight

18–19 They, he   20–21 It, he

22–23 He, she   24–25 They, him

26 dis<u>like</u>   27 <u>jump</u>ing

28 un<u>kind</u>   29 <u>fright</u>en

30 <u>passed</u>   31 al<u>together</u>

32–36 **D**avid was unsure what day it was**. W**as it **T**hursday**?**

37 sharp   38 round

39 country   40 active

Paper 6

1 merchant

2 the Arabian Sea

3 the fires

4 *He was spending all his money and would soon be very poor.*

5 decided, determined

6 *The fish was asleep; It was covered in trees and sand.*

7 He felt a small earth tremor.

8 *Surprised, frightened*

9	always	10	historical
11	also	12	already
13	mechanical	14	medical
15	accidental	16	although
17	almost	18	walked
19	jumped	20	pulled
21	sprinted	22	pushed
23	listened	24	because
25	so	26	but
27	until	28	because
29	lunch	30	itch
31	stitch	32	bench
33	pinch	34	stretch

35 voyage – a long journey

36 remedy – a cure

37 summit – the top

38 annual – every year

39 ladle – a large, deep spoon

40 fragment – a piece broken off something

Paper 7

1 stroking a moggie

2 a gas mask

3 a tray being banged

4 *She got a sinking feeling but she wasn't too worried.*

5 *Because she would be cross that Rosie had made her worry by being outside in a raid.*

6 *The state of the doors and windows told her it was a poor area; few shelters.*

7 *rich people*

8 *The light was dim; everyone was quiet because they were afraid; the noises of the person coughing and the crying baby were the only sounds.*

9	went	10	sang
11	jumped	12	fought
13	bought	14	came
15	*wild and noisy party*	16	*old, hunched teacher*
17	*beautifully clear, ice-cold pool*	18	*new born, unsettled baby*

19 *much, wet and tired children*

20	*brilliant, exciting, terrifying book*		
21	grumpily	22	poorly
23	sadly	24	quickly
25	kindly	26	happily
27	stupidly	28	roughly

29–30 York, Newcastle

31 north to south   32 at Crewe

33–34 Any two of: *Liverpool, Manchester, Sheffield, Salisbury, Exeter*

35 *excellent*

36–37 Harry, a very nervous boy, hated the thunderstorm.

38 The boys set off along the track, anxious to get to the next village before dark.

39 Najib ran as fast as he could, barely taking a breath.

40 Leena was starving, having not had anything to eat all day.

Paper 8

1 a place

2 ginger

3 fireflies

4 green balls of pepper, red skies

5 rainy and sunny

6 *They are worried about the rain, which washes away their houses.*

7 *The 'zs' in Zanzibar remind the author of buzzing bees.*

8 *Yes, because the poet says: 'I didn't know it would smell of spice'; and includes details about the rain, the children and what the evenings were like.*

9 It was Dimitri's rabbit.

10 They were Jane's crayons.

11 It was Helen's jacket.

12 It was Mop's bone.

13 It was Rajeeh's rat.

14 They were Soraya's books.

15	myth	16	gym
17	Egypt	18	mystery
19	pyramid		

20–23 reindeer, grapefruit, goldfish, sheep

24	help	25	fall
26	unhappy	27	fast

28	some	29	like
30	new	31	leave
32	hooves	33	shelves
34	loaves	35	calves
36	leaves	37	wolves

38 *My home has a swimming pool.*

39 *I have very frizzy hair.*

40 *My teacher is extremely tall.*

Paper 9

1	False	2	False
3	False	4	True
5	True	6	False
7	False		

8 The pan will run out of water/will boil dry.

9	*strolled*	10	*pleaded*
11	*grabbed*	12	*nagged*
13	*sprinted*		

14–19

words with...	
ch sounding 'sh' as in shout	ch sounding 'c' as in cat
chef	character
machine	echo
brochure	scheme

20	3	21	1
22	5	23	2
24	6	25	4
26	owl – owlet	27	cat – kitten
28	goose – gosling	29	pig – piglet
30	duck – duckling	31	bull – bullock

32–35 **T**he plane landed at **H**eathrow **A**irport a little late**.**

36–40 **T**essa and **C**laire admitted they were lost**.** **W**hat were they going to do**?**

Paper 10

1 evening

2 in a village

3 beside the woods

4–5 Two from: *the harness bells, the wind, the snow*.

6 *They are not near any houses, it is cold and dark.*

7 'The woods are lovely, dark and deep.'

8 *I would feel scared of the woods because they were dark and you couldn't see what was hidden in them.*

9	should have	10	will not
11	I will/I shall	12	cannot
13	they have	14	is not
15	would not	16	have not

17 "Have you found the dog?" asked Jim.

18 "Let's go and play in the park," suggested Aman.

19 "I don't think you have washed your face!" joked Dad.

20 "Are you enjoying the pizza?" asked the waitress.

21 "I wish it would stop raining," sighed Amy.

22 "Where do you think you are going?" asked Mrs Thrower.

23	suitable	24	reasonable
25	sensible	26	believable
27	washable	28	responsible
29	angrily	30	noisily
31	slowly	32	neatly
33	sweetly	34	loudly

35–40 overhead, moonlight, somewhere, waterfall, drainpipe, classroom

Paper 11

1 by 438 BC

2 acid rain

3 hot in summer

4–5 Two of the following: *It is very large/a lot of people live there. It is lively and busy. There is a lot of traffic. There is a lot of air pollution.*

6 It eats away at the marble of the ancient buildings.

7 It brought a new metro system and a new airport.

8 *I would not like to visit Athens as it is too crowded and polluted. I would like to visit Athens as it would be lively and fun.*

9–16 Thursday, River Thames, Kate, Queen Elizabeth, Jake, Mr Norton, September, London

A4

17–18 *Dad tried to swat the fly. Rachel went to fly her kite.*
19–20 *My football match was cancelled. Uncle Tom lit the match.*
21–22 *The ball hit Sarah in the chest. I opened the chest in excitement.*
23 its   24 It's
25 its   26 It's
27–28 It's, its
29–36 child, blind, mild, kind, behind, find, wind, wild, hind
37 elephant   38 lion
39 emu   40 giraffe

Paper 12

1 Monday
2 to pay properly
3 twelve
4 She was frightened and she hated the C.I.S.
5 She nearly threw the mobile out of the window.
6 Any one of: *Her dad had been out of work for a year. He was not in a good mood. He was tired. He was irritable and impatient.*
7 *They wouldn't understand. They would enjoy seeing her grovel.*
8 *Because she wanted to ask her mother for money and so wanted to please her first.*
9 *Child's answer reflecting on how they would deal with the situation.*
10 seen
11 bough   12 bow
13 hole   14 whole
15 meat   16 meet
17 the girl's jeans   18 my father's shoe
19 the child's toy   20 the dog's paw
21 Ravi's pencil   22 my gran's bracelet
23 treasure   24 picture
25 adventure   26 measure
27 enclosure   28 creature
29 shaggy   30–31 bright, blue
32 glistening   33 cosy

34–35 long, golden   36 *shout*
37 *stare*   38 *run*
39 *scream*   40 *feel*

Paper 13

1 mudlarking
2 coal
3 a shilling
4 *He needed low tide to hunt for coal and other things in the river.*
5 a ship
6 *Because he turned blue with cold/his hands and feet hurt.*
7 *Finding a big piece of coal.*
8 Old women (in Cotton Street or around All Saint's).
9 Any one of: *It was difficult because of the cold, the difficulty of finding coal, having to wade in the Thames barefoot.*
10–15 **A**s wendy headed to the door she called**,** "Have you seen my hat?"
16 the three dogs' collars
17 the five girls' socks
18 the nine hens' eggs
19 the two cats' bowls
20 the four dolls' beds
21 the five boys' footballs
22 the three spiders' webs
23–24 *slowly, quickly*
25–26 *peacefully, silently*
27–28 *messily, quickly*
29–30 *carefully, hastily*
31–35 antique – unique
     leaque – tongue
     through – thought
     vein – reign
     chorus – echo
36 dropped   37 hurry
38 different   39 under
40 select

Paper 14

1 feed Izzy properly
2 represent the class at the school council
3 Dwayne

4 a pet fish

5 Ben: either of: *He calmed down Mr Wilkinson; he hid Mrs Tollbart's specs.* Denzil: any one of: *He won the Tidy Books competition; he saved Izzy; he lent everyone his DVD; he asked Mr Wilkinson for afterschool football and netball.*

6 Reasons might include: *Ben was rude about him in his letter; Ben nearly killed Izzy; Ben had not returned his DVD.*

7 Either letter could be chosen, but to gain a mark the child must provide a compelling reason for their choice.

8 bananas   9 foxes

10 lorries   11 trays

12 churches   13 brushes

14 girls   15 beaches

16 First thing this morning, we met for a swim with our new friends.

17 Later that day, Daniel's gran did a magic trick.

18 Although her face didn't show it, she was very unhappy.

19 Her eyes drowsy with sleep. Fran dozed off.

20 Looking for his home, the dog ran on ahead.

21 Groping in the dark, Sam found the light switch.

22 princess   23 duchess

24 wife   25 aunt

26 she   27 niece

28 sister

29 The <u>large, brown</u> clock hung on the wall.

30 The <u>bright, loud, flashing</u> fireworks exploded in the air.

31 Sam, <u>the long-haired, shaggy</u> dog, loved going for a walk.

32 The <u>stern, pale-faced</u> teacher glared at the children.

33 Caroline's coat, <u>soaked and muddy,</u> didn't look new any more.

34 Rain poured from the <u>grey, heavy</u> clouds.

35 *I went to the park.*

36 *That bag is ours.*

37 *Give it to him.*

38 *The cup is mine.*

39 *Can they come too?*

40 *She is very fast.*

Paper 15

1 China

2 his bedroom

3 three

4 It tried to make him think his dad was being a spoil-sport.

5 His arms ached and he was out of breath.

6–7 *It was travelling very fast. It stopped in front of the sun and formed a perfect circle around Philip.*

8 *The kite moved in his hand and wagged its tail like a dog's when it sees a friend.*

9–16 gatepost, bunch, Wednesday, Tom, Edinburgh, Edward, freedom, stream

17 "Come quickly!" screamed Sam.

18 "How are you, Gran?" asked Peter.

19 "It's time to go," sighed Mum.

20 "This way to the Tunnel of Screams," directed the attendant.

21 "Have we got time?" enquired Nancy.

22 "Where are my slippers?" exclaimed Grandad.

23 here   24 gently

25 loudly   26 cheerfully

27 then   28 expression

29 information   30 discussion

31 extension   32 education

33 pollution   34 *sad*

35 *small*   36 *drop*

37 *quiet*   38 *thick/fat*

39 *below*   40 *up*

Paper 16

1 Shelborn Avenue

2 the sea

3 a tower

4 long

5 (1) Shelborn (2) River (3) Harbour (4) Oaktree (5) Mill

6 River Road

7 Ride a bike

8 58 Mill Road, Denton

9 Pirates

10 although **11** than

12 so **13** but/although

14 if **15** and

16 bub/ble **17** pad/dle

18 flan/nel **19** ken/nel

20 ar/rive **21** sad/dle

22 bur/row **23** cab/bage

24–31

	add 'er'	add 'est'
short	shorter	shortest
high	higher	highest
small	smaller	smallest
slow	slower	slowest

32 s©ene **33** dis©ipline

34 fas©inate **35** cres©ent

36 snow – cow **37** pull – skull

38 ear – wear **39** wave – have

40 bough – trough

Paper 17

1 no

2 some of them

3 Billy

4–5 *They call him names. They make up jokes about his mum.*

6 *They don't really mean it*

7–9 *lonely, upset, angry*

10 hand + bag

11 sun + light

12 candle + stick

13 shoe + lace

14 tooth + paste

15 dust + bin

16 post + box

17–22

re	de	pre
replay	deflate	prehistoric
revisit	demist	precaution

23–24 *You must not disturb this bird's chicks.*

25–26 *The boy stole that girl's sweets.*

27–28 *Can we use those boys' pencils?*

29–33 Antony likes playing football.
Brian likes painting.
Brian likes craft lessons.
The other boys like Antony.
Antony would rather play cricket than stay indoors.

34–40 nouns – Thursday, scream
adjectives – windy, loud
verbs – walking, heard
adverbs – briskly

Paper 18

1 the fashion for longer hair and beards

2 she did not have enough to eat

3 a palm tree

4–5 *Two from: he needed to get some money; he was stung by his wife's words; he did not like being hit with a broom.*

6 *The barber was disturbing him by being on his territory.*

7 *His legs shook, his hair stood straight up, his teeth chattered.*

8 *He remained calm/he was able to think clearly.*

9 *The barber would use the mirror to show the ghost its reflection to make it think the barber had captured another ghost.*

10 aircraft **11–12** scissors, clothes

13 bison **14** sheep

15–20 poisonous hideous curious
tremendous jealous humorous

21 ! **22** ?

23 ! **24** ?

25 ? **26** !

27 ! **28** ?

29–34 camcorder, DVD player, cinema, astronaut, television, microwave

35–40

Pronouns about others	Pronouns about myself
yours	me
hers	I
theirs	mine

Bond English Assessment Papers 8–9 years

1 going to catch a bus
2 nervous
3 twilight
4 *He couldn't keep his hands still.*
5 *The assistants were taking things out of the window.*
6–7 *The witness was not quite sure of the time and could not remember the colour of the man's hair.*
8 *The witness says that the tall man was wearing the baseball cap, but earlier the witness said the small man was wearing the baseball cap.*
9–10 Aman has to buy carrots, potatoes, rice and tomatoes at the shop.
11–13 At the park Geri, Meena, David, Jason and John all play together.
14–15 On Mark's way to school he passes the police station, the swimming pool, the park and the shops.
16–17 At the farm the children fed the goats, stroked the pigs, milked the cows and brushed the horse.

18–25

	add 'er'	add 'est'
hot	hotter	hottest
tall	taller	tallest
big	bigger	biggest
thin	thinner	thinnest

26 droplet
27 duckling
28 bullock
29 booklet
30–35 **M**ax asked. **"I**s it time **J**ess got out of bed**?"**
36 their
37 There
38–39 Their, there
40 There

1 ask no questions
2 smugglers
3 brushwood
4 midnight
5 Brandy, 'baccy, laces, letters, barrels of brandy-wine.
6 *So that you don't see the smugglers.*
7 tar and ropes
8 *The poem refers to 'your mother' and uses the phrases 'my darling' and 'for your play'.*
9 friendship
10 neighbourhood
11 motherhood
12 apprenticeship
13 It's
14 its
15–16 It's, it's
17 its
18 its
19 It's
20 It's
21 *the long, warm coat*
22 *the huge, grey elephant*
23 *the fast, red car*
24 *the giant, pointed skyscraper*
25 *the gnarled, old tree*
26 *the hard boiled egg*
27 *the limp, wilting flower*
28 because/after
29 but/because
30 after/and
31 and/so
32 so/and
33 but
34 and/because
35 herd
36 adult
37 sleepy
38 cautious
39 error
40 soon

A Visitor's Guide to Athens

Athens is one of the oldest of all cities. Named after Athena, the Greek goddess of wisdom, its history stretches back over 3000 years. It is home to one of the world's most famous buildings. The white marble temple, the Parthenon, sits on a hill right in the centre of the city. It can be seen for miles around. It took about eight years to build and was completed in   5
438 BC. It is one of the main reasons why tourists visit Athens.

However, when visitors come to modern Athens for the first time they are rather surprised by what they find. Athens is very big. About 4 million people live there. It is a lively, modern, busy place with many urban problems. There are huge traffic jams in the city's streets and   10
considerable air pollution. Sometimes the smog is so thick that it is almost impossible to see the Parthenon on its hill. Acid rain is eating away at the marble of the ancient buildings and has already caused irreversible damage.

Fortunately in the last few years there have been some improvements   15
in the air quality. In preparation for the Olympic Games, which were staged in Athens in 2004, the city built a new metro system. The rail network carries 400,000 passengers a day. It is estimated to have removed 200,000 cars from the streets. For the Games Athens also built a wonderful new airport on the edge of the city.   20

Athens has very hot summers. In July and August the average daytime temperature is 31°C. Athenians tend to stay out late at night when it's cooler. No one eats much before 9 pm, and many shows and entertainments don't start until midnight. You need to be able to stay up late in Athens! Winters, on the other hand, can be quite cold and the city   25
has snowfalls most years. The best times to come are spring and autumn – and there's lots to do: museums, art galleries, restaurants and nightlife. And if you get tired of it all, take the metro to the city's port and hop on a boat to one of the hundreds of Greek islands where you can lie in the sun and get away from the crowds.   30

Underline the right answers.

    1 When was the Parthenon built?

    (by 438 BC, 3000 years ago, we don't know)

    2 The ancient buildings are damaged by (tourists, earthquakes, acid rain).

    3 The climate in Athens is (wet, warm all the year round, hot in summer).　◯ 3

Answer these questions.

    4–5 List two things that surprise visitors to Athens.

    _____

    _____

    6 Why is acid rain so damaging?

    _____

    7 What benefits did the 2004 Olympic Games bring to Athens?

    _____

    8 Explain why you would or would not like to visit Athens, using information from the visitor's guide.

    _____　◯ 5

Underline all the **proper nouns**.

9–16 ten   Thursday   River Thames   cat   Kate   lunch

    Queen Elizabeth   tonight   Jake   Mr Norton

    September   line   London　◯ 8

Write two sentences for each **homonym**. In each sentence the homonym must have a different meaning.

17–18 fly

    (1) _____

    (2) _____

19–20 match

(1) _____

(2) _____

21–22 chest

(1) _____

(2) _____

⬤ 6

Add *its* or *it's* to fill the gap in each sentence. Don't forget to use a capital letter where necessary.

23 The cat jumped out of _____ bed.

24 "_____ time we went to school," called Mum.

25 The elephant drank through _____ trunk.

26 "_____ Sophie at the door, Amy," Dad shouted.

27–28 "_____ autumn and time the tree lost _____ leaves," commented Nathan.

⬤ 6

Find eight words in the wordsearch ending in *ild* or *ind*.

b	c	h	i	l	d	t
l	g	k	n	d	s	a
i	g	o	w	t	j	f
n	r	f	i	i	h	i
d	m	i	l	d	n	n
k	i	n	d	s	e	d
s	b	e	h	i	n	d

29–36 _____ _____ _____ _____

_____ _____ _____ _____

⬤ 8

Add the missing **consonant letters** to each word to make a wild animal.

37 e__e__ __a__ __   **38** __io__

39 e__u   **40** __i__a__ __e

⬤ 4

Now go to the Progress Chart to record your score!   Total ⬤ 40

Mia is being bullied at school by a gang called the C.I.S.

On Saturday morning they woke me up at a quarter past seven.

Their text message was short and not at all sweet.

PAY UP ON MON OR ELSE   5

After seeing that I couldn't stop shaking. In the end I put the blankets over my head and curled up tightly into a ball.

Oh how I hated their messages. Hated them, hated them, HATED THEM. In fact,   10
I nearly got up and threw my mobile out of the window. Then I stopped myself, because that would have been a daft thing to do – and anyway, they'd just love me to do that.   15

So instead I lay under my covers worrying about Monday ... What were we going to do? We'd joked about handing them fake money or giving them the five pounds all in two-pence pieces. But I was pretty certain we'd hand over the money. It seemed the easiest and safest option – for now.

I had just one problem with that. I was flat broke.   20

I'd insisted on paying Oliver back the four pounds he'd loaned me. And the rest – which wasn't much – I'd spent on sweets and a magazine.

Of course, I could ask Oliver to lend me another five pounds. And I knew he would. But that just seemed to be taking advantage of his good nature. What else could I do? Well, I could always try and explain to the   25
C.I.S. that I only get twelve pounds a month pocket money. And remind them again that my dad was out of work for a year.

It would all just be a waste of my breath, though. Chris Freyer would enjoy seeing me grovel to her. But she wouldn't understand. That chip on her shoulder was so huge it blotted out everything else. So it seemed I   30
had no choice but to put out the begging bowl to my parents.

My dad was home now, but he was not in the best of moods. I think he was just dead tired with his new job and all the training he'd just done, but he was kind of irritable and impatient. Then, in the afternoon he took my two little brothers swimming: this was the moment to work on   35
my mum.

To butter her up I offered to do the hoovering downstairs. I did it extra thoroughly too.

From *Traitor* by Pete Johnson

Underline the right answers.

1 The gang told Mia to pay on (Monday, Tuesday, Wednesday, Thursday).

2 She decided (not to pay, to give them fake money, only to pay in two-pence pieces, to pay properly).

3 For pocket money she got (four, five, twelve) pounds a month.

Answer these questions.

4 Why couldn't Mia stop shaking?

_____

5 What did Mia nearly do?

_____

6 Why was it hard to ask her dad for money?

_____

7 Explain in your own words why it was a waste of time explaining to the gang that she could not pay.

_____

8 Why did Mia do the hoovering extra thoroughly?

_____

9 What would you do if you were being asked for money?

_____

Underline the correct **homophone** in the brackets.

10 I have never (seen, scene) so many people there.

11 The (bough, bow) of the tree had broken off.

12 The man gave the queen a graceful (bough, bow).

13 There was a big (hole, whole) in the ground.

14 The (hole, whole) school went to see the play.

15 The dog ate the (meet, meat) in his bowl.

16 Jess said she'd (meet, meat) Callum at the park.

Write the following lines in a shortened form, using the apostrophe.

Example: the glove belonging to the lady   *the lady's glove*

17 the jeans worn by the girl   _____

18 the shoe belonging to my father   _____

19 the toy the child had   _____

20 the paw of the dog   _____

21 the pencil Ravi owned   _____

22 the bracelet belonging to my gran   _____   6

Add sure or ture to these letters to make a word.

23 trea_____   24 pic_____

25 adven_____   26 mea_____

27 enclo_____   28 crea_____   6

Underline the **adjectives** in each sentence.

29 The shaggy dog panted loudly.

30–31 Tom's bright blue coat suited him well.

32 The glistening raindrops hung on the branches.

33 Naomi slept in her cosy bed.

34–35 Donna's long, golden hair had all been cut off!   7

Write a more powerful **verb** for each of these verbs.

Example: take   *grab*

36 say   _____   37 look   _____

38 walk   _____   39 call   _____

40 touch   _____   5

Paper 13

This story is set in Victorian London. Jamie and his friends make a living hunting for scraps beside the Thames.

Low tide was early next morning.

I'm a mudlark. I make my money by picking up the coal that falls out when they're unloading the brigs. I have a little basket strapped to my back. Sometimes I fill it twice in a day. Not that often, though.

I'm a good worker. I go out mudlarking even in the winter when most of the others can't stand the cold. It was only me and Davies and Ten Tons and maybe Patty and a couple of others by Blackwall pier this winter. Ten Tons and me are fine with it, but Davies turns blue with cold. I'm tougher than Davies, even though he's stronger than me. I can work all day even in the winter, when you have to crack the ice to lever the coals out of the mud. It's all Davies can do to sit on the bank and shiver and cry because his hands and feet hurt so much.

Sometimes the coal lies on the surface of the mud, but often it sinks under. Then you have to feel in the thick mud with your toes and hands. It's exciting when you find a big piece, but it's usually little nibs. When the basket's full I take it and sell my coal to the old women up and down Cotton Street or around All Saint's.

We don't just pick up coals, we pick up anything that gets dropped, just about. You get a farthing a pound for old iron. You get ha'pence for bits of rope. If you find fat the cooks have dropped overboard you can get three farthings for that. For good new copper, you can get up to four pence a pound.

Most things can be sold in this world. Once I made a shilling in a day. Mostly it's more like seven or eight pence.

5

10

15

20

From *The Copper Treasure* by Melvin Burgess

Underline the right answers.

1 What word is used to describe what the children in the story do?

(treasure hunting, mudlarking, scavenging)

2 What are they looking to find in the river?

(coal, gold, rubber)

3 What was the most Jamie ever made in a day? (four pence, a shilling, seven pence, eight pence).

3

Answer these questions.

4 Write in your own words why low tide was important to Jamie.

_____

5 What is a 'brig' (line 3)?

_____

6 Why did Davies find it so hard to work in winter?

_____

7 What excited Jamie when he was out mudlarking?

_____

8 Who bought the coal from Jamie?

_____

9 Explain in your own words why mudlarking was so hard.

_____

6

Write this sentence again, adding the missing punctuation and capital letters.

10–15 as Wendy headed to the door she called have you seen my hat

_____

_____

6

Add the missing apostrophes to these **plural nouns**.

Example: the six boys books   the six boys' books

16 the three dogs collars   _____

17 the five girls socks   _____

18 the nine hens eggs   _____

19 the two cats bowls   _____

20 the four dolls beds   _____

21 the five boys footballs _____

22 the three spiders webs _____ ⟨7⟩

Next to each **verb** write two **adverbs** that could describe it.

23–24 walk _____ _____

25–26 sleep _____ _____

27–28 eat _____ _____

29–30 draw _____ _____ ⟨8⟩

31–35 Match the words with the same spelling patterns using a line.

antique   echo

league   reign

through   unique

chorus   thought

vein   tongue ⟨5⟩

Underline a **synonym** for the word in bold.

36 fell	dropped	flew	rose	felt
37 rush	blow	bump	knock	hurry
38 unlike	different	same	unkind	similar
39 beneath	above	beyond	away	under
40 choose	like	eat	select	present

⟨5⟩

Now go to the Progress Chart to record your score! Total ⟨40⟩

Vote for Ben Barton!

Just writing to let you know it's time to choose the Form Captain again. Yes, I know it's a dreadful bore thinking about it, but to save your tiny brains the effort, I've got a dead simple solution – vote for me, Ben Barton, the number one choice for Form Five.

Why? Easy! Who came top of exams last year? Who's the leading goal scorer in the school team? Who knows how to calm Mr Wilkinson down when he's in a mood? Who hid Mrs Tollbart's specs so she couldn't mark our homework last week? Who will represent you best at the school council, as long as you pay me (just joking!)? Who can do juggling tricks with the bean bags?

And just think what the alternatives are! Sally Hunt – the biggest airhead in the class? Dwayne 'the Gorilla' Smith? I don't think so. Denzil Steel-Perkins? With a name like that he'd better stay class librarian. There's really only one choice – me! So vote, vote, vote for Brainy Ben, I say!

Dear Fellow Class Members

I'm writing to ask for your vote in the elections for Form Captain. I realise it's hard to decide who to vote for. It's easy to choose your best friend, or the person who shouts loudest, but it's best to choose someone who will help the whole class. I'd like to give you five reasons for considering me.

1   I kept the class library in perfect shape last year so that we won the Tidy Books competition.
2   I saved Izzy from eating himself to death when someone (whose initials begin with BB) put too much food in his water tank.
3   I lent everyone in the class my Supertronics DVD last term, though I'm still waiting for it back from The Person Who Overfed Izzy.
4   I will campaign for an extra five minutes at break time.
5   I have already asked Mr Wilkinson if we can have afterschool footie and netball.

Whoever you vote for, I'll still be your friend.

Best wishes

Denzil

Underline the right answers.

1 Which of these things can Ben not do?

(play football, juggle, feed Izzy properly, calm down Mr Wilkinson)

2 The form captain has to:

(tidy the library, feed Izzy, represent the class at the school council, juggle beanbags).

3 Who was called 'the Gorilla'?

(Sally, Denzil, Dwayne, Izzy, Ben)

○ 3

Answer these questions.

4 Who or what is Izzy?

_____

5 List something each boy has already done to help the class.

Ben _____

Denzil _____

6 Explain in your own words why Denzil might not like Ben.

_____

7 Whose letter is more persuasive? Give reasons for your choice.

_____

○ 4

Write each of these **nouns** in their **plural** form.

8 banana _____   **9** fox _____

10 lorry _____   **11** tray _____

12 church _____   **13** brush _____

14 girl _____   **15** beach _____

○ 8

Add the missing comma to each of these sentences.

16 First thing this morning we met for a swim with our new friends.

17 Later that day Daniel's gran did a magic trick.

18 Although her face didn't show it she was very unhappy.

19 Her eyes drowsy with sleep Fran dozed off.

20 Looking for his home the dog ran on ahead.

21 Groping in the dark Sam found the light switch.

○ 6

Underline the feminine word for the word in bold.

22 **prince**	fairy	woman	princess	queen
23 **duke**	player	actress	lady	duchess
24 **husband**	mother	father	wife	aunt
25 **uncle**	nephew	aunt	niece	sister
26 **he**	her	him	them	she
27 **nephew**	uncle	niece	cousin	woman
28 **brother**	sister	mother	child	twin

7

Underline the **adjectival phrase** in each sentence.

29 The large, brown clock hung on the wall.

30 The bright, loud, flashing fireworks exploded in the air.

31 Sam, the long-haired, shaggy dog, loved going for a walk.

32 The stern, pale-faced teacher glared at the children.

33 Caroline's coat, soaked and muddy, didn't look new any more.

34 Rain poured from the grey, heavy clouds.

6

Use each of these **pronouns** in a sentence.

35 I

_____

36 ours

_____

37 him

_____

38 mine

_____

39 they

_____

40 she

_____

6

Maybe none of it would have happened if Philip had listened to his father's warning not to play with the kite on his own. Maybe. But who can tell with magic?

'It's big enough to blow you away,' his mother said when she saw the kite.

Philip laughed. Nobody had ever been blown away on a kite – not even on one as huge as this. His uncle had brought it back as a present from China and it really was the biggest and best you'd ever seen. It was shaped like a dragon and was coloured red, yellow and green.

Philip wanted to go out and fly it at once but his father said he had to wait until the weekend. The weekend! That was a whole four days away.

Philip put the kite in the corner of his bedroom. Every time he looked at it, he heard a voice whispering in his head.

'Go on,' the voice said, 'it's your kite. Dad's just a spoil-sport. Go on – it'll be good fun. No one will know if you sneak out for half an hour.'

For two days Philip managed to say 'no' to the voice, but on the third day he gave in …

The kite was so big that his arms ached from holding it up so that it didn't touch the ground. It was so big that by the time he reached the top of the hill in the park he was out of breath …

He looked up. A small, round, black cloud was racing across the blue sky. It was moving faster than any cloud Philip had ever seen. He felt the kite move in his hand. The long dragon's tail wagged from side to side like a dog's when it sees a friend.

The cloud got nearer and nearer the sun. Philip saw its shadow come racing up the hill towards him. It grew darker and Philip waited for the shadow to pass. But when he looked up, the cloud had stopped, directly in front of the sun. Its shadow formed a perfect circle all around him.

Then, out of nowhere came the wind. Whistling and spinning and howling. Philip closed his eyes. He felt his arms rise up above him as the wind caught the kite and lifted it. For a moment, he thought of letting go but there was a sudden tug and it was too late.

From *Beaver Towers* by Nigel Hinton

Underline the right answers.

1 The kite came from (Peru, China, France, America).

2 Philip kept the kite in (the garage, the kitchen, his bedroom).

3 Philip gave in to the voice after (four, three, two, five) days.

(3)

Answer these questions.

4 What did the voice try to make Philip think about his father?

_____

5 How did Philip feel as he carried the kite to the park?

_____

6–7 What two things were very unusual about the cloud's behaviour?

(1) _____

(2) _____

8 What, in the story, tells you that there was a connection between the kite and the cloud?

_____

(5)

Circle words that are **nouns**.

9–16   gatepost   happy   bunch   laughed

Wednesday   greasy   sadly   Tom

Edinburgh   Edward   freedom

stream   famous   fought

(8)

Rewrite these sentences, adding the missing speech marks.

17 Come quickly! screamed Sam.

_____

18 How are you, Gran? asked Peter.

_____

19 It's time to go, sighed Mum.

_____

20 This way to the Tunnel of Screams, directed the attendant.

_____

21 Have we got time? enquired Nancy.

_____

22 Where are my slippers? exclaimed Grandad.

_____

⬭ 6

Choose the most suitable **adverb** from the words below to put in each space. Each word may only be used once.

cheerfully   then   gently   here   loudly

23 The soldier stood _____, guarding the palace.

24 The nurse removed the dressing _____.

25 The ducks in the pond quacked _____.

26 The old man _____ greeted his friend.

27 The boys pushed past her _____ ran off laughing.

⬭ 5

Add the **suffix** *ion* to each word, but be careful as some letters may need to be removed or added.

Example: explode + ion   = explosion

28 express + ion   = _____

29 inform + ion   = _____

30 discuss + ion   = _____

31 extend + ion   = _____

32 educate + ion   = _____

33 pollute + ion   = _____   6

Write an **antonym** of each word.

34 happy _____   **35** large _____

36 catch _____   **37** noisy _____

38 thin _____   **39** above _____

40 down _____   7

Dear Gail

As you live near me in Denton, here are directions for getting to my party on foot:

* Go out of your gate. Turn left. Go to the end of Shelborn Avenue. Turn right into River Road. Go as far as the post-box. Cross the road there. (Be careful. Cars come fast up the road.) Go down the footpath opposite, past the horse field. (Usually two old ponies in there, very keen on carrots!)

* At the end you're in Harbour Road. Don't take the right to the sea front. Turn left, go past St James Church with the spire, cross the road again, take the third right into Oaktree Road. (There's a house with a red gate just before the turn.) Go about 90 metres until you see a sign on the right hand side that says 'Public Footpath, no bicycles'. Don't take this. Just beyond there's another path between two very tall houses. It's not marked at all.

* Go down there, over the footbridge. When you get to the end, you're in our road, Mill Road. It's a very long road, so you've still got a way to go.

* Turn left. Keep going until you see the second church, St John's, on the right, with a tower. Our house is seven beyond that, number 58. It's got a holly hedge and balloons outside.

* It should take you about 20 minutes. Any problems just ring on your mobile. Our number is 552961.

See you there!

Imran

P.S. I'm sure everyone in Denton will think you wearing a pirate hat in public is quite normal!

Underline the right answers.

    1 Gail lives in (Harbour Road, Mill Road, Shelborn Avenue, River Road).

    2 Gail lives near (a motorway, the sea, a supermarket).

    3 St John's church has (a tower, a spire, a flag).

    4 Mill Road is (long, dangerous, straight).

    4

Answer these questions.

    5 Write down these roads in the order that Gail will travel along them:

        Oaktree, River, Harbour, Mill, Shelborn.

    (1) _____   (2) _____   (3) _____

    (4) _____   (5) _____

    6 Where would you go to post a letter?

    _____

    7 What can't you do on the footpath in Oaktree Road?

    _____

    8 What address does Imran live at? Include the name of the town.

    _____

    9 What was the fancy dress theme for the party?

    _____

    5

Put one of the **conjunctions** in each of the spaces below.

        but   although   than   and   if   so

    10 He tried to open the door _____ he had seen the man lock it.

    11 I would rather have a cup of hot tea _____ drink a mug of cold coffee.

    12 I cut my hand _____ I put a plaster on it.

    13 Joe wanted to buy some sweets _____ he hadn't brought enough money.

    14 I shall wear a T-shirt _____ it is a warm day.

    15 The girls are going hiking _____ swimming.

    6

Rewrite these words, drawing a line to separate the **syllables**.

Example: yellow   yel/low

16 bubble _____

17 paddle _____

18 flannel _____

19 kennel _____

20 arrive _____

21 saddle _____

22 burrow _____

23 cabbage _____

8

Complete this table of comparing **adjectives**.

24–31

	add 'er'	add 'est'
short		
high		
small		
slow		

8

Circle the silent letter in each of these words.

32 scene

33 discipline

34 fascinate

35 crescent

4

With a line, match the words that have the same letter string (group of letters) but which make a different sound.

36 snow   have

37 pull   trough

38 ear   skull

39 wave   cow

40 bough   wear

5

Paper 17

Billy Doesn't Like School Really

Billy doesn't like school really.
It's not because he can't do the work
but because some of the other kids
don't seem to like him that much.

They call him names
and make up jokes about his mum.

Everyone laughs ... except Billy.
Everyone laughs ... except Billy.

They all think it's OK
because it's only a laugh and a joke
and they don't really mean it anyway
but Billy doesn't know that.

Billy doesn't know that
and because of that
Billy doesn't like school really.

by Paul Cookson

Underline the right answers.

1 Does Billy like school?
   (yes, no, don't know)

2 How many children don't like Billy?
   (all of them, some of them, none of them)

Answer these questions.

3 Who doesn't laugh in this poem?

4–5 What two things do the other children do to Billy?

   (1) _____

   (2) _____

2

6 Why do all the children think it is OK to have a laugh and a joke?

_____

7–9 Write three words describing how you would feel if you were Billy.

_____   _____   _____

7

Write the two small words each **compound word** is made from.

10 handbag   =   _____ + _____

11 sunlight   =   _____ + _____

12 candlestick =   _____ + _____

13 shoelace   =   _____ + _____

14 toothpaste =   _____ + _____

15 dustbin   =   _____ + _____

16 postbox   =   _____ + _____

7

Write these words, depending on their **prefix**, in the table below.

deflate   replay   demist   prehistoric   revisit   precaution

17–22

re	de	pre

6

Write each of these **phrases** in a sentence and don't forget the missing apostrophe.

23–24 this birds chicks

_____

25–26 that girls sweets

_____

27–28 those boys pencils

_____

6

Antony likes outdoor games; he is very popular with the other boys, and he is untidy and noisy. Brian is artistic and he likes making things. He is neat and quiet.

Underline the correct sentences.

29–33 Antony likes playing football.
Brian's books are not very tidy.
Brian likes painting.
Antony is a quiet, tidy boy.
Brian likes craft lessons.
The other boys like Antony.
Antony would rather do woodwork than play cricket.
Brian is often told he must not make so much noise.
Antony would rather play cricket than stay indoors.

(5)

Copy any **nouns**, **adjectives**, **verbs** and **adverbs** found in the sentence below.

34–40 While walking briskly on a windy Thursday I heard a loud scream.

nouns _____

adjectives _____

verbs _____

adverbs _____

(7)

A long time ago there lived a poor barber. The barber was poor because
not enough people seemed to want their hair cut or their beards
trimmed. This was the fashion at the time. The barber's wife was always
complaining that she didn't have enough to eat. She would say to her
husband, 'If you did not have enough money to support a wife, why did   5
you marry me? When I was in my father's house I had plenty to eat, but
here there is never anything in the larder.' Then she would take a broom
and beat the poor barber until his back was quite blue.

   One day, the barber was so stung by his wife's words – not to mention
the broom – that he decided to leave the house and vowed never to   10
return until he became rich. He packed a bag and set off, trudging the
road from village to village, until he came to the edge of a forest. His feet
ached, so he lay down in the shade of a tall tree to bemoan his hard lot.
'I must be the most unhappy barber in the land,' he moaned, 'perhaps in
the whole world.'   15

   As the barber said this, something stirred in the branches of the tree
above him. You see, this tree was the home of a ghost, and ghosts
don't like people coming near their territory. As the ghost floated down,
it spread its long white arms and stood like a tall palm tree before the
barber, its gaping mouth hanging wide open. 'Barber, you must suffer for   20
disturbing me,' cried the ghost. 'I am going to destroy you, you miserable
person.'

   The barber had never seen a ghost before, so he behaved as most
people do when they first see one. His legs shook and the hair on his
head stood straight up like the bristles on his wife's broom. But although   25
he was frightened, the barber kept his head. 'Oh, ghostly spirit,' he said
through chattering teeth, 'I wonder whether you will destroy me when I
show you what I have in my bag?'

'Stupid barber,' replied the ghost, 'how can the contents of your bag prevent me destroying you?' But he was an inquisitive ghost too, and he added, 'Let me see what you have in your bag; then I will strike you dead.' 30

The barber slowly opened his bag. 'I hardly dare to say this to you, ghost, but my bag is full of ghosts I have captured during the last few days. In fact, there is barely room for one more ghost in here before I take them home for my good wife to make into ghost soup. When I have 35 captured you, ghost, and squeezed you into my bag, I'll be on my way.' So saying, the barber took from his bag the mirror he used to enable his customers to see whether their beards had been trimmed to their taste.

From *Ghost Soup* by John Paton

Underline the right answers.

1 The barber was unsuccessful because of (his lack of skill, the low price for cutting hair, the fashion for longer hair and beards).

2 The barber's wife was angry because (she wanted to stay with her father, she did not have enough clothes, she did not have enough to eat).

3 The ghost looked like (a black shape, a white sheet, a palm tree).

◯ 3

Answer these questions.

4–5 Give two reasons why the barber left home.

(1) _____

(2) _____

6 Why was the ghost angry with the barber?

_____

7 Describe what happened to the barber's body when the ghost spoke to him.

_____

8 What is meant by 'the barber kept his head' in line 26?

_____

9 What do you think the barber's plan was?

_____

_____

◯ 6

Underline the **noun** or nouns in each sentence which use the same word in their **plural** and **singular** form.

10 The aircraft flew high in the sky.

11–12 The dressmaker used her scissors to cut the fabric for the clothes.

13 The tourists watched the bison from their coach.

14 The steep Welsh slopes are home to the sheep.

5

Circle the ous words that have been spelt correctly.

15–20   poisonous   couragous   curious

jealous   hideous   dangeous

serrious   humorous

tremendous

6

Put a question mark or exclamation mark at the end of each sentence.

21 Catch the thief_____

22 Shall we look in this shop_____

23 Don't do that_____

24 Why does Dad snore so loudly_____

25 Can we go swimming now_____

26 Hurry up, time is running out_____

27 Listen, a siren_____

28 Please may I have a sweet_____

8

Circle the words that wouldn't have been widely used a hundred years ago.

29–34 camcorder DVD player donkey

cinema   doctor   astronaut   television

candle   microwave   cloth

6

Put the **pronouns** in the correct columns in the table.

me   yours   hers   I   mine   theirs

35–40

Pronouns about others	Pronouns about myself

6

Now go to the Progress Chart to record your score!   Total   40

58

A witness's report on the robbery

It was about 5.20 pm, though I can't be sure of the exact
time. My watch is a few minutes fast. I was walking down
Nelson Street on my way to the bus stop. There were not many
people around. The shops were getting ready to close and the
streetlights were starting to come on. I was hurrying for the   5
bus but must have missed it, as there was no one waiting at
the stop.

I just stopped to tie my shoelace up when I saw two men
come by. I looked at them carefully, for some reason. It was
something about the way they behaved. They looked nervous.   10
One of the men was quite tall. He was wearing a raincoat
and blue jeans. I can't remember the colour of his hair but do
remember that he couldn't keep his hands still. He must have
been about 35 or 40. The other man was shorter, and in his
twenties I'd say. He had a blue baseball cap on, with the   15
word 'Italy' written on it. He didn't look very Italian to me, he
was too fair. He was whispering to the tall man, who was still
fidgeting. The men seemed like they were waiting for someone
or something.They were outside Smithards the jewellers. The
lights were still on inside, but I could see the assistants starting   20
to take the rings, brooches and watches out of the window, so
they must have been about to close.

The men stood there for a moment, looking uncertain what
to do. Then the tall man said 'Now!' He must have said it quite
loudly, because I'm a bit deaf and I definitely heard it.   25

Immediately the men ran towards the shop and burst through
the door. There was a shout from inside, then some screams. An
alarm started to go off somewhere. It was incredibly loud and
before I knew what was happening I heard police sirens coming
up the street. Just then the men came crashing out of the shop.   30
The tall man in the baseball cap was carrying a bag in his hand.
As they tumbled into the street, they saw the police cars and
just ran for it as fast as they could.

Underline the right answers.

1 The witness was (shopping, coming home from work, going to catch a bus).

2 The two men looked (untidy, nervous, hurried, frightened).

3 It was (daylight, morning, night, twilight).

3

Answer these questions.

4 What does the taller man do that shows he was nervous?

_____

5 How did the witness know the shop was about to close?

_____

6–7 List two things that the witness was not sure about.

_____

_____

8 The witness seems to have made a mistake in describing the men when they came out of the shop. What was it?

_____

_____

5

Add the missing commas in each sentence.

9–10 Aman has to buy carrots potatoes rice and tomatoes at the shop.

11–13 At the park Geri Meena David Jason and John all play together.

14–15 On Mark's way to school he passes the police station the swimming pool the park and the shops.

16–17 At the farm the children fed the goats stroked the pigs milked the cows and brushed the horse.

9

Complete this table of comparing **adjectives**. Some words need their last letter doubled before adding the **suffix**.

18–25

	add 'er'	add 'est'
hot		
tall		
big		
thin		

8

Complete each word to make a **diminutive**.

ling   let   ock

26 drop_____   27 duck_____

28 bull_____   29 book_____

4

Write this sentence again, adding the missing punctuation and capital letters.

30–35 max asked is it time jess got out of bed

_____

_____

6

Write *their* or *there* in each of the spaces below. Don't forget to start with a capital letter if necessary.

36 The children went to play with _____ friends in the swimming pool.

37 _____ isn't going to be any rain today.

38–39 _____ shoes are over _____ on the floor.

40 _____ was a huge bang as the fireworks exploded.

5

A Smuggler's Song

If you wake at midnight, and hear a horse's feet
Don't go drawing back the blind, or looking in the street,
Them that asks no questions isn't told a lie.
Watch the wall, my darling, while the Gentlemen go by!
Five and twenty ponies
Trotting through the dark –
Brandy for the Parson,
'Baccy for the Clerk;
Laces for a lady, letters for a spy,
And watch the wall, my darling, while the Gentlemen go by!

Running round the woodlump if you chance to find
Little barrels, roped and tarred, all full of brandy-wine,
Don't you shout to come and look, nor use 'em for your play.
Put the brushwood back again – and they'll be gone next day!
If you see the stable-door setting open wide,
If you see a tired horse lying down inside;
If your mother mends a coat cut about and tore;
If the lining's wet and warm – don't you ask no more!

From *A Smuggler's Song* by Rudyard Kipling

Underline the right answers.

1 Which of these things does the poem tell you to do?

(draw back the blind, look out in the street, ask no questions, shout out if you find barrels)

2 Who are the Gentlemen?

(soldiers, smugglers, rich men, lords)

3 What are the barrels covered with?

(coats, brushwood, straw, grass)

◯ 3

Answer these questions.

4 What time would the smugglers be likely to come?

_____

5 What things might the smugglers bring?

_____

6 Why does the poem tell you to watch the wall?

_____

7 What are the barrels secured with?

_____

8 How can you tell this poem is written to a child rather than a grown-up?

_____

◯ 5

Add the **suffix** *ship* or *hood* to each of these words.

9 friend_____   **10** neighbour_____

11 mother_____   **12** apprentice_____

◯ 4

Add *its* or *it's* to fill the gap in each sentence. Don't forget to start with a capital letter if necessary.

13 _____ a beautiful day.

14 The cat played with _____ ball.

15–16 _____ time you remembered your own bag, _____ not that hard!

17 Everyone was lined up outside the school; _____ fire alarm was going.

18 Will's dog lost _____ ball.

19 _____ got to be here somewhere!

20 _____ been a brilliant party. I wish I could have one every week!

8

Write a **phrase** (group of words) that could describe each of these **nouns**.

Example: bed   the soft, feathery, comfortable bed

21 coat _____

22 elephant _____

23 car _____

24 skyscraper _____

25 tree _____

26 egg _____

27 flower _____

7

Use one of the following **conjunctions** in each gap.

but   and   so   after   because

28 I missed the train _____ I overslept.

29 Ahmed is in the cricket team _____ Josh wasn't good enough.

30 Mum wrapped up my present _____ I went to bed.

31 Jake bought some toffees _____ Mike got some too.

32 Cathy's sewing is untidy _____ she will have to do it again.

33 I like macaroni _____ my brother likes spaghetti better.

34 The sky was blue _____ the sun was shining.

7

Match the words to their **definitions**.

soon   sleepy   error   cautious   herd   adult

35 group of cattle   _____

36 grown-up   _____

37 heavy-eyed   _____

38 careful   _____

39 mistake   _____

40 in a short time   _____   6

Now go to the Progress Chart to record your score!   Total   40

Progress Chart   English 8–9 years

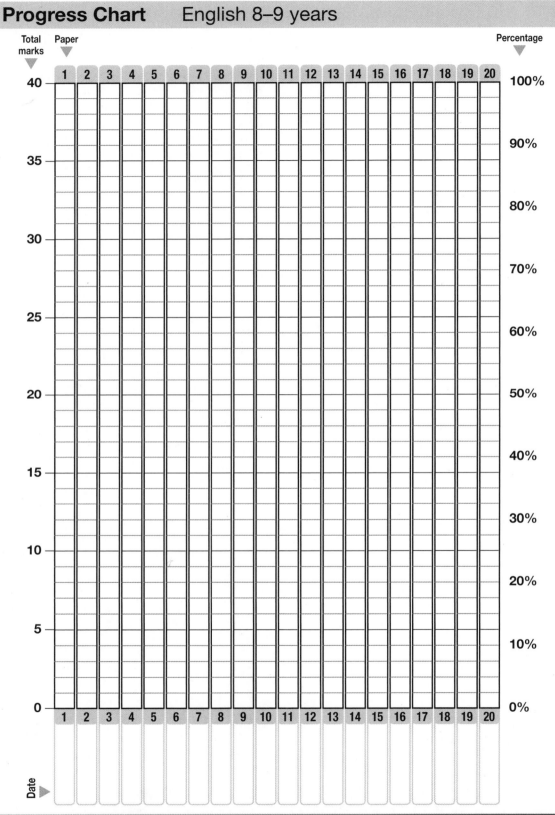

When you've finished the book read the Next Steps